A.MOLE
I LOVE
GRAVI-TEA

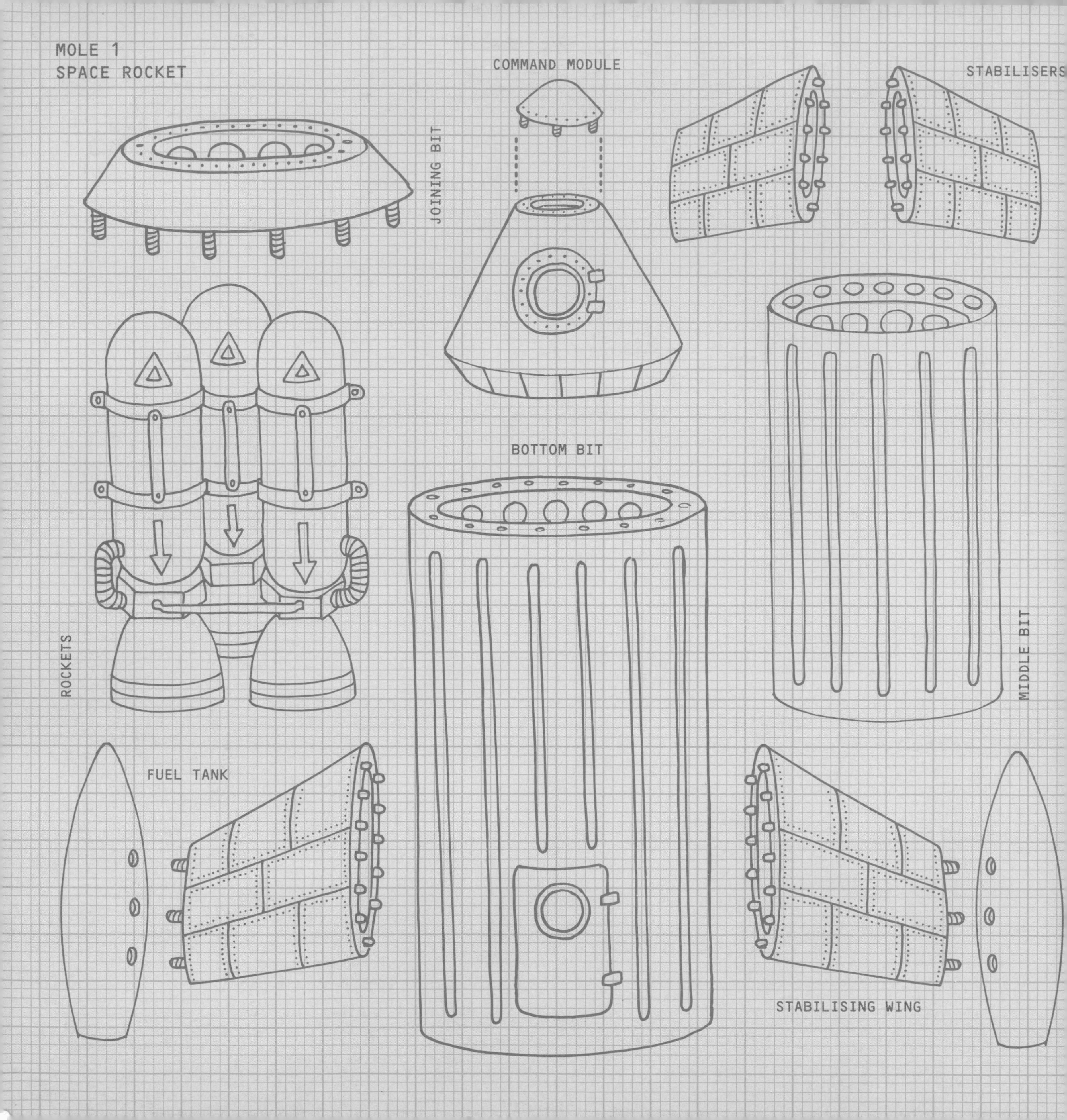
MOLE 1
SPACE ROCKET
COMMAND MODULE
STABILISERS
JOINING BIT
BOTTOM BIT
ROCKETS
MIDDLE BIT
FUEL TANK
STABILISING WING

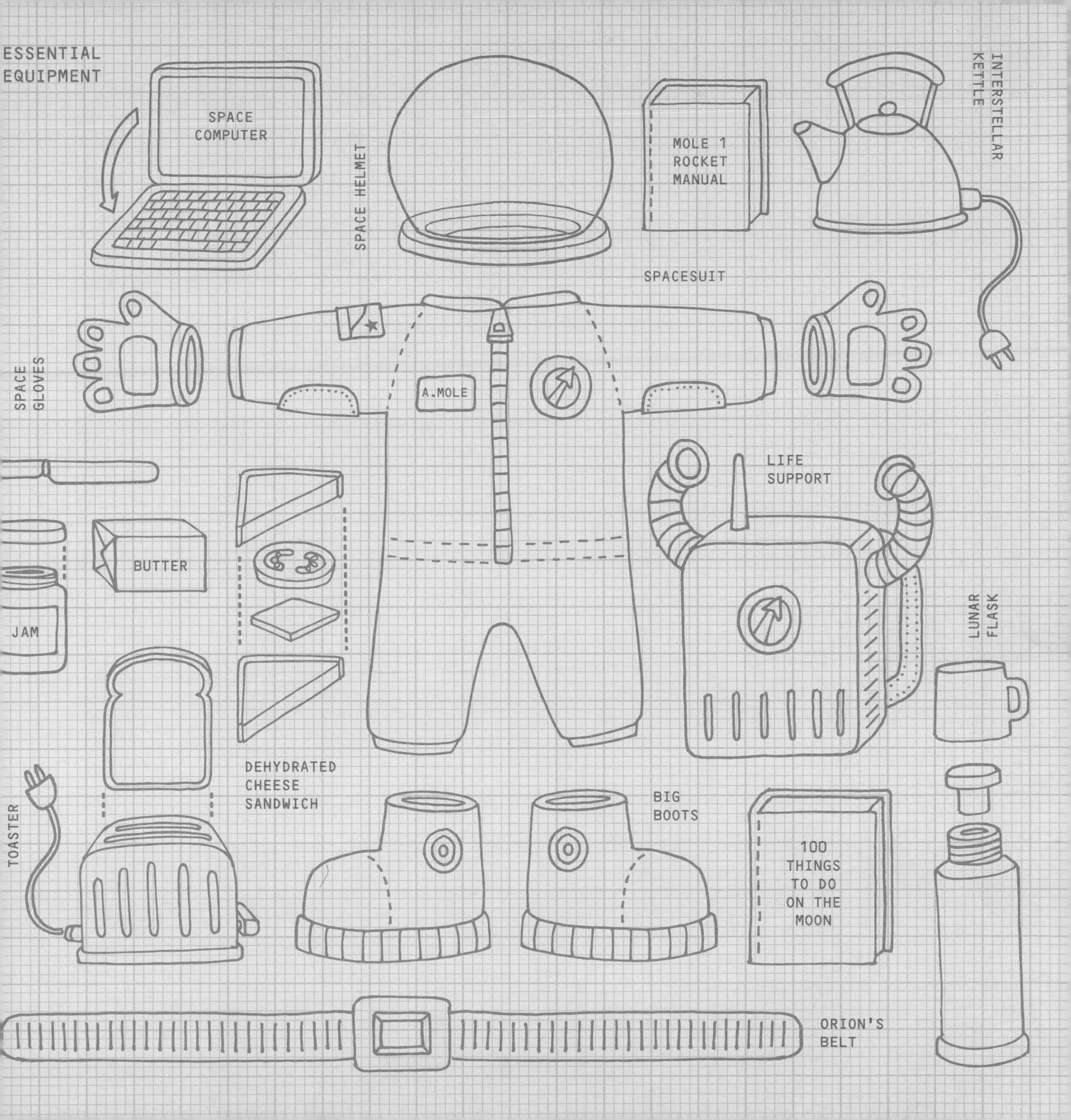
ESSENTIAL EQUIPMENT
SPACE COMPUTER
SPACE HELMET
MOLE 1 ROCKET MANUAL
INTERSTELLAR KETTLE
SPACESUIT
SPACE GLOVES
A.MOLE
LIFE SUPPORT
BUTTER
JAM
LUNAR FLASK
DEHYDRATED CHEESE SANDWICH
BIG BOOTS
TOASTER
100 THINGS TO DO ON THE MOON
ORION'S BELT

First published in 2019 by
Scholastic Children's Books
Euston House, 24 Eversholt Street,
London NW1 1DB

A division of Scholastic Ltd

www.scholastic.co.uk

London ~ New York ~ Toronto
Sydney ~ Auckland ~ Mexico City
New Delhi ~ Hong Kong

ISBN 978 1407 18786 0

Printed in China

10 9 8 7 6 5 4 3 2 1

Papers used by Scholastic Children's Books
are made from wood grown in sustainable forests.

For AUGIE!
May you have
many adventures.

ROCKETMOLE

MATT CARR

SCHOLASTIC

Armstrong the mole was fed up
with living underground.
It was dark, damp and dirty...
...and a bit boring.
HOLE SWEET HOLE
DIG SPORT
MOLECHESTER CITY RUIN PITCH AGAIN
DAILY DIG

But BORING is what moles do!

laughed his friend Mona.

You see, Armstrong was

A STAR-NOSED MOLE.

Instead of
digging down,
he preferred
to look UP.

He was also a clever
and inventive mole.

He built himself
a telescope AND made
some glasses so
he could look
through it!

WOW!

Armstrong yearned for adventure.

One night he tunneled up
to the surface to look
at the moon.

It was amazing, glowing brightly
in the night's sky.

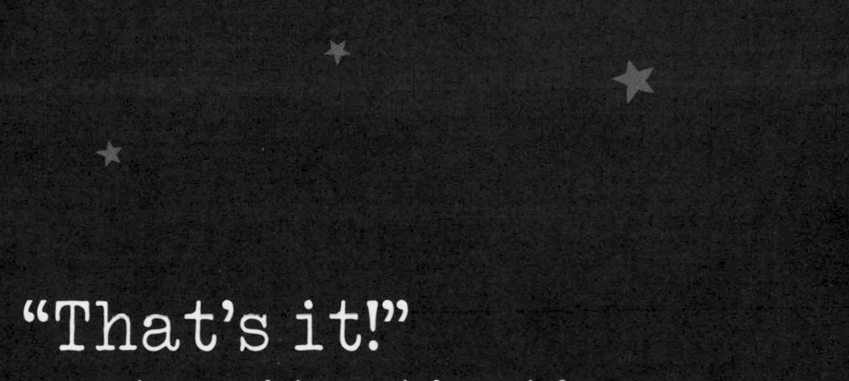

"That's it!"
he said to himself.

"I'm going to go to the moon!"

Armstrong called a mole-meeting
to tell all his friends.

"Don't be silly!" said Doug.
"We moles stay underground
because it's SAFE down here."

Armstrong didn't care about danger,
he was a MOLE ON A MISSION!

I'm boldly going
where no mole has
gone before!

But he soon found out that getting a small mammal into orbit wasn't that easy!

...VERY BIG!

Armstrong worked day and night until he'd made the biggest rocket any mole had ever built!

(In fact it was the only rocket any mole had ever built.)

MOLE 1

Even his friends were impressed as they bravely peeked up above the ground to watch the countdown.

It's out of this world!

It will be in a minute!

The rocket zoomed into space at incredible speed!

The journey to the moon was long and dangerous. But floating around in zero gravity was fun, although drinking tea was a bit of a struggle!

(And the less said about going to the toilet the better.)

After a few days, Armstrong reached the moon.

He leapt out full of excitement!

HOORAY!

He'd made it!

Armstrong was the first mole on the moon!
He felt very proud.

He would've patted himself on the back
but his spacesuit was too tight!

A. MOLE

Armstrong began to explore.

He bounced around for a bit...

But the novelty soon wore off.
The moon was not that different from home...

It was dark and cold...

...and a bit boring.

MOLE 1

Suddenly Armstrong felt very small.

He sat down for a spot of lunch.

The world looked so beautiful, with its oceans, lands and fluffy clouds.

"I miss the earth AND I miss my friends,"

he sighed.

He tried to eat his dehydrated cheese sandwich but he couldn't get it past his space helmet.

It's time to go HOME.

...and landed with a **BUMP!**

He was about to go underground to find his friends when...

... they surprised **HIM!**

They'd plucked up the courage and ventured above ground to welcome him home.

"You're an inspiration to us all!"

said Maggie.

"You've shown that if you're brave enough to follow your dreams, anything is possible."

"It's **ONE GIANT LEAP** for molekind!"
chuckled Armstrong.

The welcome home party was brilliant but Armstrong looked glum.

"I've been to the moon. Now I want to see the WORLD!" he said, "But it's no fun on my own."

ARMSTRONG
FIRST MOLE ON THE MOON!

His friends already felt bigger and braver. "Don't worry, we'll come with you!" they all cried.

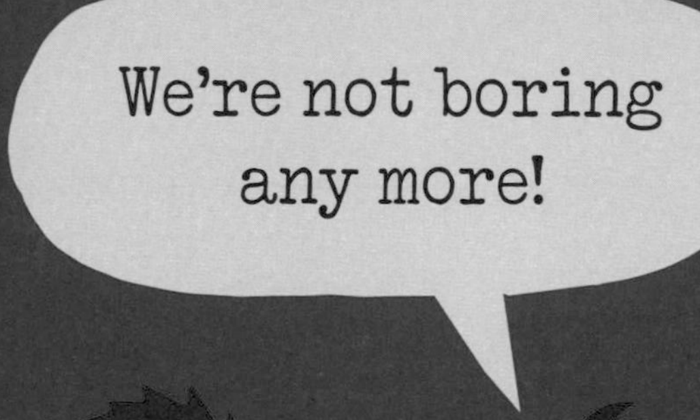

We're not boring any more!

SLURP!

That's IT!
Armstrong had a great idea!
If I recycle the rocket it might just work!

And so Armstrong built an amazing underground BORING machine and set out on a brand new adventure. This time with all his friends on board!
MOLE 2
I'm outta here!

LET'S GO!

We've got a HOLE world to explore!

NEW YORK, USA
Come on, we're going shopping!
WOW!
Bonjour!
PARIS, FRANCE
MAASAI MARA, KENYA
Don't worry, I'm sure it will be perfectly safe up there.
Have an ice day!
ANTARCTICA
ARMSTRONG

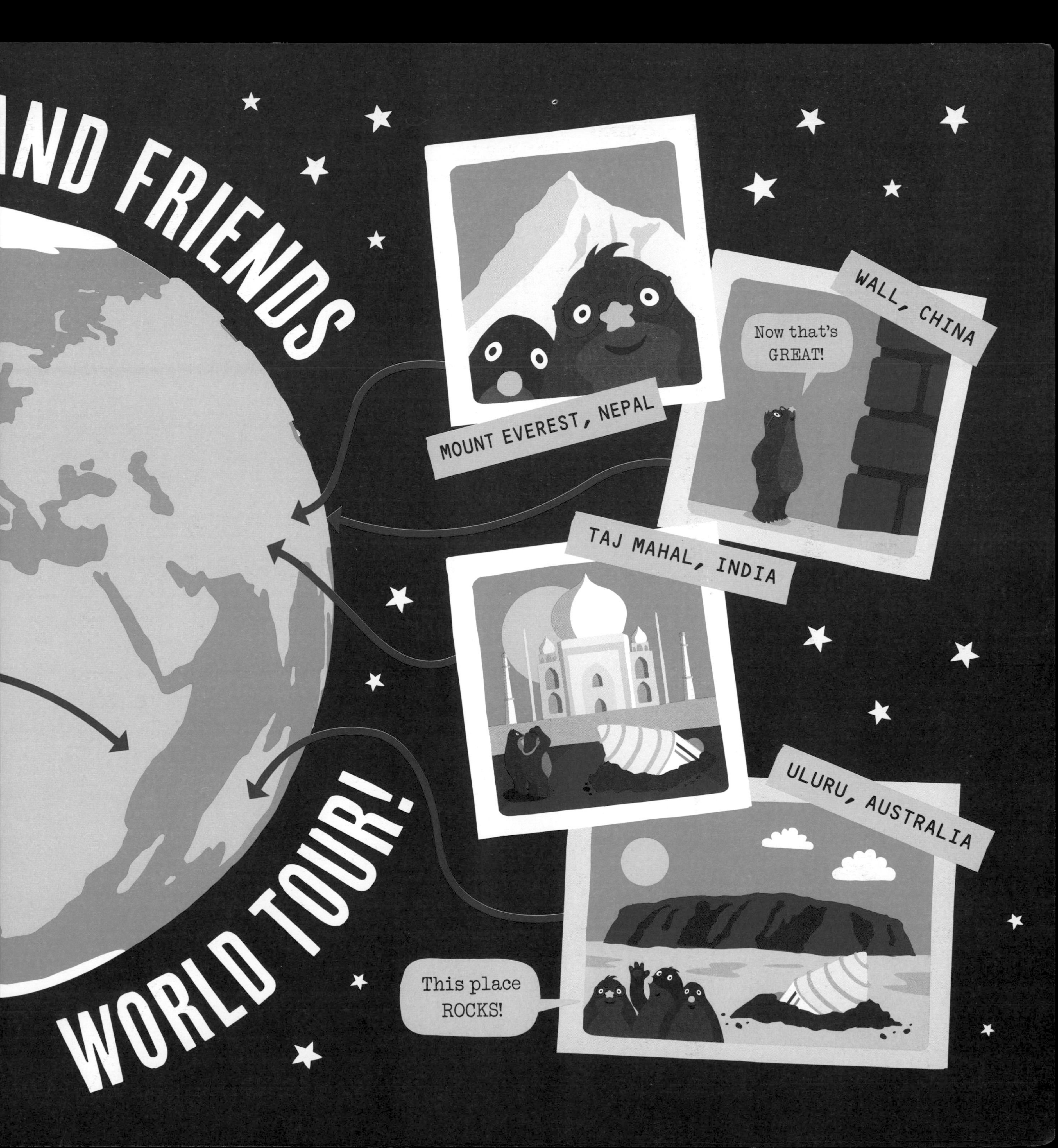
AND FRIENDS
WORLD TOUR!
MOUNT EVEREST, NEPAL
WALL, CHINA
Now that's GREAT!
TAJ MAHAL, INDIA
ULURU, AUSTRALIA
This place ROCKS!

MAGNIFICENT
MOLE FACTS!

Moles get everywhere! Almost. They are found on every continent except Antarctica and South America.

Moles live underground most of the time but they can sense light.

Moles love eating earthworms and can eat their bodyweight in a single day!

Moles travel around through tunnels, but they also make bedrooms and kitchens where they store and eat their worms.

Star-nosed moles use their strange 'snout' to feel around for food.

The moon orbits the earth roughly once a month.

The moon has a huge number of craters which are caused by comets and asteroids crashing into it!

The moon affects the tides of the seas and oceans and even helps make waves.

The first person on the moon was the American Neil Armstrong on the Apollo 11 mission in 1969.

MARVELLOUS
MOON FACTS!